Finally add a bit more detail, as in our examples, and colour in your doodle if you like. That's it!

Grab your pencils and paper and get started. You'll soon have some fantastic Deadly Doodles to put on your bedroom wall.

Happy Doodling

Nicola. Jo
Mike Méhellexx

Killer Bees

Skill Level: Medium

Most bees can sting, but killer bees are more aggressive than ordinary honeybees. They are quick to attack anything that disturbs them and they chase their enemies in greater numbers than other bees and for longer distances.

3. Now go over your pencil outlines with a marker pen to make big bold lines. Add little lines over the head for the antennae and draw in the eyes and stripes.

2. Add a couple of lines at the end of the body for the sting. Then add two teardrop shapes for the wings.

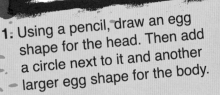

1. Using a pencil, draw an egg shape for the head. Then add a circle next to it and another larger egg shape for the body.

4. To make your cartoon killer bee look really deadly, colour it in with black pen.

Tiger

Skill Level: Medium

Biggest of the big cats, the tiger is a superb predator with deadly claws and sharp teeth. Amazingly, each tiger has a slightly different stripe pattern – no two are exactly the same.

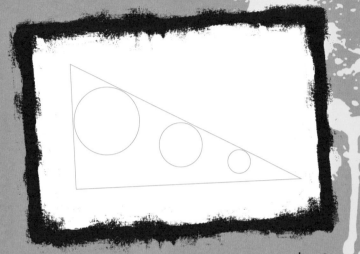

1. Using a pencil, draw a big triangle as above. Inside the triangle, draw a big circle, a medium circle and a small one for the head.

2. Draw three arrow shapes under the big circle and three slanting lines under the middle circle.

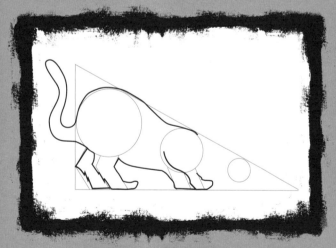

3. Now join up the shapes. Using a marker pen, draw a gently curving line from the middle circle over the back and up to make the tiger's tail. Using the arrows as a guide, draw in the legs and paws. Make the lines a bit jagged so that your tiger looks furry.

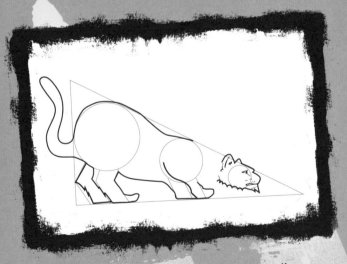

4. Your tiger is about to pounce and is really alert so draw his ears sticking up on top of the small circle. Add a bump for his brow, then draw in a snarling mouth, some long whiskers and an eye.

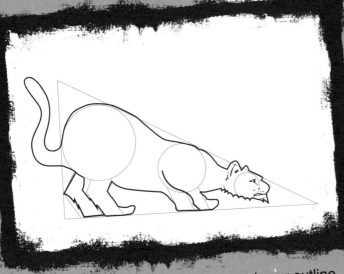

5. Join the tiger's head to the body and your outline is complete. You can rub out the pencil lines now if you like.

6. It's time to add the stripes! Every tiger has a different pattern so be creative and have fun adding the stripes to your deadly tiger.

DEADLY

Piranha

Skill Level: Easy

This fish may be only 30 centimetres long, but it has razor-sharp, triangular-shaped teeth and can strip meat off bones with amazing speed. A creature to avoid!

1. Start by drawing a half-circle in the middle of your page. Add a triangle for the top fin, then two more for the side and tail fins.

2. Add a circle in the middle for one eye and a half-circle for the other eye.

3. Starting under the eye, add another triangle to make the fish's lower jaw.

4. Go over the fins with a black marker, adding zigzag lines and some detail inside for the spines. Make a nice thick black line around the eyes and add a small 'C' shape to each one for the pupils. Draw more zigzag lines on the top and bottom jaws for the sharp teeth. Lastly, add mean eyebrows over each eye.

Brown Bear

Skill Level: Medium

It might look cuddly, but the brown bear is one of the largest meat-eating land animals. A male can weigh over 500 kilograms – more than six people. Brown bears eat lots of berries and nuts, but they can also attack and kill large animals such as deer and moose.

1. Start by drawing a horizontal line towards the top of your doodle area. Then add a deep cup shape at each end of the line.

2. Draw another horizontal line between the cup shapes. Then add a kind of rectangular shape on the side.

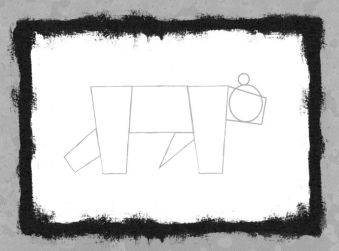

3. Draw a circle inside the rectangular shape and add a smaller circle on top for the bear's ear. Add another cup shape sticking out at the back and then draw a little triangle under the lower horizontal line.

4. Take a brown marker pen and start to go over your outlines. Make your lines slightly jagged to create a rough furry look and round them out, as shown above, to make the body shape. Add some shading inside the ear and claws on the feet. Draw in a little tail.

5. You can rub out your pencil lines now if you like, before finishing off your bear doodle.

6. Next, add some shading with dark brown and lighter brown pencils. Working inside your outlines, add some nice messy strokes with your pencils to make the bear's body look more realistic.

Fish Eagle

Skill Level: Easy

Strong and speedy, this ferocious eagle has wings that can measure an incredible 2 metres from tip to tip. When the eagle spots a fish, it swoops down to the water surface and seizes its prey in its strong curved talons with amazing speed.

1. Start by drawing a circle for the eagle's head and an egg shape for the body. Add two triangles for the legs. At the end of each leg, draw three tiny egg shapes for talons, with another underneath.

2. For the wings, draw a rectangle on each side of the body. Add a little triangle under the head to make the beak.

3. Add some lines at the sides of the wings to help you draw in the feathers. Draw a triangle under the body for the tail.

4. Using a marker pen, go over your pencil outline. Make your lines slightly jagged to give a feathery look. Add a line of zigzags across the breast, then draw in nostrils and some menacing eyes. Draw big swooping lines for the wings, following your guidelines, then add a zigzag base to the tail.

5. Now it's time to add some colour! Go round the edges with a brown pastel, then add some lighter brown and a little bit of yellow.

6. Starting at the tips of the wing feathers, use your fingers to blend the colours. Lastly, add some yellow to the eagle's beak and talons.

DEADLY

Chameleon

Skill Level: Medium

The cunning chameleon sits on a branch as it watches for prey, holding on tight with its specially adapted feet and tail. When an insect comes close, the chameleon shoots out its long, sticky-tipped tongue, traps the prey and swallows it – all in a fraction of a second.

1. With your paper upright, draw a big egg, then a smaller one inside it for the head. Make sure they join at the bottom.

2. Add two circles for the eyes and a triangle on the head. For the branch, draw a small circle and join it to the body with two lines

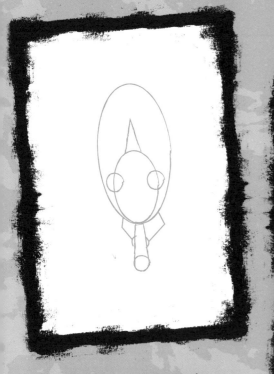

3. Add two lines between the body and branch to make the arms. Add two little half-moons at the ends for the hands.

4. Starting at the side of the body, draw a big spiral for the chameleon's tail.

5. Grab a marker pen and go over your pencil outline. Keep your marker lines nice and loose to give movement.

6. Add a line to complete the tail and join it to the body. Then add zigzag lines for the mouth and some shading in the eyes.

7. Take some coloured crayons and colour in your chameleon. Use circular scribbling movements to give the effect of the scales on its body.

Crocodile

Skill Level: Medium

The world's biggest reptile, the saltwater crocodile can grow to 7 metres or more. Its huge, powerful jaws contain 66 sharp teeth for seizing hold of its prey and tearing off chunks of flesh.

1. This doodle is made up of letters. Start by drawing a big letter 'C' for the head. Then add two more 'C' shapes for the body.

2. Then add two smaller 'C' shapes on each side, as shown, for the legs.

3. Draw a really big 'Z' for the mouth and a sideways 'Z' to make the lower jaw. Then add the curly tail.

4. Now add the ridges on the croc's back. Start at the tail and draw in two lines in each section, making them slightly wider apart as you get nearer the head. Draw an eye on the side of the crocodile's head.

5. Take your marker pen and go over your pencil lines to make them really bold. Add some 'V' shapes for the feet and claws and then draw some sharp teeth in the jaws.

6. Add some bold shading under the jaw and body, then make the eyes look mean by adding shading and some more lines underneath. Add in some lines to give the body a rough, scaly look.

Redback Spider

Skill Level: Easy

The female redback spider has a very venomous bite and it's one of the few spiders that is dangerous to people. Redbacks make an amazing web with sticky trip lines that hang down to the ground, ready to trap prey.

1. Start by drawing a large circle for the spider's body. Then add a smaller, slightly overlapping circle for the head.

2. Add two little egg shapes for the eyes. Place them at an angle to help make the spider look angry.

3. Draw in four legs and feet at each side of the body, as above. Then carefully rub out the lines through the eyes and the line across the head.

4. Now take a black pencil and add the deadly fangs. Make them big and fierce-looking.

5. Go over the lines with your black pencil. Make the legs thicker and add little ovals to make the feet. Add dots to the eyes. Shade the edges of the body to make it look furry.

6. Take your red pencil and add the diamond-shaped marking on the back that shows this is a deadly redback. And there's your cartoon spider!

Lynx Skill Level: Easy

This prowling, pouncing predator is the largest cat in Europe. Its excellent hearing and sharp teeth help it to catch animals that are three or four times its size, such as deer.

1. Draw a big hill in the middle of your paper. Add two triangles for the ears and a cup shape for the mouth. Draw a triangle for the nose and two more for the eyes.

2. Using a black marker, add in some detail. Draw round the ears, giving them more shape and add a line to make the flap. Add some tufts at the tips of the ears.

3. For the fur around the lynx's head, draw some simple zigzag shapes at the top of the head and add some larger zigzags at the sides. Go over the pencil lines for the mouth with your marker pen.

4. Draw a big box inside the mouth shape and add in those big sharp teeth, two at the top and two smaller ones at the bottom. Add a little shading inside the mouth. Go over the nose and eyes in marker pen and add lines linking the nose to the eyes. Draw in some extra-thick lines over the eyes.

5. Add little lines inside the eyes for the pupils and draw in some markings around the eyes – a bit like eyelashes. Then add a line either side of the nose to emphasise the top of the mouth.

6. To finish off your doodle, draw some little dots and long lines on either side of the nose for the whiskers. Then add in a little shading on the nose of your ferocious-looking lynx.

DEADLY

King Cobra

Skill Level: Medium

This cobra measures 5 metres – longer than a family car – and is the longest venomous snake in the world. Its main prey is other snakes! When hunting, the cobra strikes quickly, injecting large amounts of venom into its prey with its deadly fangs.

1. Using a pencil, start by drawing a large heart shape. Then below that draw a slightly smaller oval shape.

2. Add a pointed claw shape – this will be the cobra's tail. In the middle of the heart, add a diamond shape. Then draw two wiggly lines from the diamond to the bottom of the oval.

3. The cobra's face will be inside the diamond. Draw in some nice big fierce eyes. Add a wiggly line below the lines, then draw two big sharp fangs.

4. Now get your black marker pen and start going over your pencil lines. Don't worry if some of them still show – you can rub them out later.

5. Add some shading inside the mouth so it looks like the snake has its mouth open, ready to attack. To make the hood, add lines inside the heart as shown. Finally, add some lines across the body to show the snake's curving shape.

First published in Great Britain in 2012
by Orion Children's Books
a division of the Orion Publishing Group Ltd
Orion House
5 Upper St Martin's Lane
London WC2H 9EA
An Hachette UK Company

1 3 5 7 9 10 8 6 4 2

A catalogue record for this book is available from the British Library.

ISBN 978 1 4440 0640 7

Printed and bound in Italy by Printer Trento

www.orionbooks.co.uk